PEGGY'S COVE

NOVA SCOTIA

Photographs by
Sherman Hines

Dedicated
to the memory of
William de Garthe.

© Sherman Hines, 1992

Nimbus Publishing Limited
P.O. Box 9301, Station A
Halifax, N.S., Canada
B3K 5N5

Design: Jackie Ranahan
Printing and Binding:
Everbest Printing Company, Limited, China

All photographs by Sherman Hines
Camera and film used:
Pentax 6 X 7
2 1/4" X 2 3/4"
Fujichrome

Canadian Cataloguing in Publication Data
Hines, Sherman, 1941 —
        Peggy's Cove

ISBN 1-55109-009-0

1. Peggy's Cove (N.S.) - Description - Views.
1. Title.

FC2349.P53H56 1992   917.16'22   C92-098504-1
F1039.5.P53H56 1992

INTRODUCTION

By Alex Newman

Perched at the edge of the world and a short drive from Halifax, is a spot so beautifully simple it defies definition. If we could include, with these vivid images by Sherman Hines, the shrill cries of the seagulls, the thunder of surf running high, or a whiff of salt and fish and seaweed, we might have captured the essence of Peggy's Cove. But we can only hope to show you what is there through these photographs, capturing the sea and the rocks and the sky one moment at a time.

What sets Peggy's Cove apart from all the other picturesque fishing villages on the Lighthouse Route is its particular juxtaposition of rock and sea. At one time, it was the rocks, carried along with the ice and deposited like enormous pebbles in the wake of the last Ice Age, that intruded upon the shore. But now the sea is the aggressor, pounding the rocks mercilessly with spray and spume so forceful it has pock-marked those great granite slabs which resolutely face St. Margaret's Bay.

The cove beckons whilst it forbids. Rock and surf cause us to stand back in reverence, but the cove's oval construction, 300 yards long and half that width, draws us closer, like a magnet, to its narrow mouth, the source where granite meets brine amid moss and weeds and foam.

Against this mighty panorama, the inhabitants of Peggy's Cove dare to impose themselves, appearing all the more vulnerable in contrast to the magnitude of the ocean and the stretch of granite. Wooden fishing stores and stages (like docks) are ravaged by time and water, yet their spiky pillars hold firm. Fishermen's houses, framed by neat boxed gardens of rose coloured "orchids" and purple-crimson pitcher plants, maintain a respectful distance from the sea and rocks. The village's simple order and cheerful existence rimming the cove shows not oblivion to the sea's wild whims but an awareness that human life continues within an appropriate context of nature.

When you arrive at the cove, something opens up. You want to be friendly, to move out of yourself. You may find yourself running free, scrambling over rocks, the wind in your face, tangling your hair. Where else could one want to go? To be?

As you pass around the cove, you must ascend a steep rise before you come upon the lighthouse, a beacon rising straight and stark against the horizon sky. The cove itself is nestled protected in the lee of the granite rocks that take all the bluster of the sea upon their great shoulders. Behind the homes lie the stubby patches of hayfields used long ago. In days gone by, this hay would dry in the sun, scattered across the rocks surrounding the cove like golden stubble on a young man's·beard. It used to be that children would wait at the village gate to open it for visitors and obtain a nickel or dime tip.

But many things change and the children no longer act as porters, the hay is no longer strewn about the rocks and many fishing families have gone. Artists, who have lingered over the beauty, remained to document beauty's changing face and have converted fishing houses and stores into studios.

Ahead lies the glittery sea, and the shimmer of rock, and the church standing high and brazen in a sun-bright sky, and reef after reef jutting tenuous fingers from the rocky coast into St. Margaret's Bay. The pungent salt air, redolent of newly caught fish, assails the nostrils. The silence and stillness is broken by seagulls, with their cacophony of shrill screams and swift, macabre flying dances of flapping wings and frenzied sudden downward dips in search of fish entrails.

The fog, sometimes as thick and fluid as a stage curtain, can roll in and wipe out sun and scene in one fell swoop. It starts with the horizon line, once so sharp and clear, then the shore, the lighthouse, the buildings, until it has you wrapped in its filmy grip, and you can see no further than your own toes and you are reminded how small and insignificant nature makes you.

The sea's moods are as mercurial as the weather and it can change from benign cheer to violent rage. The rain then drives in sheets off its blue-grey turgid surface and its spray lashes the rock-bound shore. After the storm, when the sea's anger abates, the surf is still high and, with a tide well in, the breakers unrelenting. It is another mood and it too will change, but the sea must be awarded its due respect, for it takes as victims the defiant and foolhardy.

The endless wrestling between rock and sea has helped forge resolute, sturdy characters, with little regard for anything but the authority of nature. The people of Peggy's Cove embrace the sea as passionately as the rocks do and, perched tenuously here at the edge of the ocean, it has become a microcosm of Nova Scotia's history. Pirates and privateers were intimately familiar with places to hide along Nova Scotia's craggy eastern shore. The first settlers — Scotch, Irish, French — made part of their living from the sea. When Nova Scotia fishermen had free entry into the New England market before Confederation, the price of fish was high and life was good at the cove, as it was in all of Nova Scotia. Population soared to three or four hundred people and the fish stores and stages were flush against one another in a solid rim the half mile around the cove. And now there is tourism — life in the cove has kept apace, in its own way, with the changing times.

Talk here is still on the weather. To the sea, all weather is good weather but to those who must deal with the weather — fisherman, artist, tourist — it is everything.

Peggy's Cove remains an active fishing village.
Far Right: Rays of sunlight reflect through a shower of surf.

Lobster traps dot
the docks and
shoreline of the
cove, year round.

Above: Fishermen process the day's catch.
Left: Photographer and tourist, Monte Zucker, stops to admire the picturesque cove.
Overleaf: The old Garrison store.

Houses and fish
stores overlook the
daily activity in the
cove.

Winter in the cove.
Overleaf: The sun casts its golden glow over the lighthouse.

Far left: Ice forms on a tide pool. Left and Overleaf: Images such as these are part of the reason that Peggy's Cove continues to be a favoured subject for artists.

Completed in 1916, the present day lighthouse has always been a welcomed sight to the fishermen of the cove.

Far left: The aftermath of the wind and fury of an Atlantic storm. Left: Even in the coldest of weather, the fishermen brave the elements to set out their lobster pots.

Above: Quiet
reflections.
Right: Ice covered
rocks.

Reflections of
evening light.
Overleaf: The
Peggy's Cove
wharf, built in 1939.

Above photos left to right:
Crook's Gift Shop, William
de Garthe's home and art
gallery, The Sou'Wester
Restaurant and Gift Shop,

Beal's Bailiwick Gift Shop,
decorative duck decoys, gifts.
Right: The warm glow of
shops greet the tourists.

Far left: St. John's Anglican Church, completed in 1885. Left: Magical moods of Peggy's Cove. Overleaf: William de Garthe's monument to the fishermen and their families of Peggy's Cove. Ten years in the making, the granite sculpture behind de Garthe's home depicts thirty figures.

Above: The monument and the man. The late William de Garthe at work on his tribute to the fishermen and their families of Peggy's Cove.
Right: Activity on the wharf.
Overleaf: The mighty surf.

Above: Vignettes of Peggy's
Cove.

The weather extreme. Overleaf: Tranquility in the cove at sunset.

Above: Fog rolls
into the peaceful
cove.
Right: Love is
present in the
evening light.

Left: Sunset truly is one of the most satisfying parts of the day.

The lure of the sea.
The mystery of the sea.
The spirit of Peggy.

BUILDING THE
BRIDGE
TO P.E.I.

Harry Thurston

Photography
Wayne Barrett and
Anne MacKay

NIMBUS
PUBLISHING

Nimbus Publishing Limited

PO Box 9166

Halifax, Nova Scotia B3K 5M8

(902) 455-4286

Design: Kate Westphal, Graphic Detail, Charlottetown, PEI

Printed and bound in China

Canadian Cataloguing in Publication Data

Thurston, Harry, 1950-

   Building the Bridge to PEI

   ISBN 1-55109-260-3

1. Confederation Bridge (PEI).   I. Barrett, Wayne.   II. MacKay, Anne.   III. Title.

HE377.C32P7 1998   388.1'32'09717   C98-950014-4

Acknowledgements:

The text is based on articles by the author that first appeared in *Canadian Wildlife*, November/December 1996 ("A Bridge too Far?") and *Canadian Geographic*, March/April 1997 ("Strait Across"). The author thanks the editors of these magazines for their assistance.

Lines by Milton Acorn are from the poem "The Island" in *The Island Means Minago*. 1975. NC Press, Toronto.

Special thanks to Kevin Pytyck, Krista Jenkins, Alan Davison and the many people who worked for Strait Crossing Inc., also Gerard Sexton, Marine Atlantic and Fenton Maritime Agency.

Front cover: The completion of Confederation Bridge signals the dawn of a new era on Prince Edward Island.

Facing page: On June 1, 1997, Confederation Bridge, linking Prince Edward Island to the mainland, replaced 80 years of continuous car ferry service between Borden, PEI and Cape Tormentine, NB.

Overleaf: A marvel of cold ocean engineering, Confederation Bridge, or the fixed link as it is commonly called, is the longest bridge in the world over ice-covered waters.

Nimbus Publishing acknowledges the financial assistance of the Canada Council and the Department of Canadian Heritage.

I

LONG ROAD TO A FIXED LINK

A SHORT HISTORY OF THE BRIDGE

The longest bridge in the world over ice-covered waters. The fulfilment of a century-old promise to Prince Edward Islanders. And the stepping stone to a new era of Island life. Confederation Bridge—the 12.9 kilometre fixed link between Cape Jourimain, New Brunswick, and Borden, Prince Edward Island—is all of these things.

The bridge opened on schedule, on May 31, 1997, with much fanfare. Some 20,000 people walked and ran across the bridge to take part in opening celebrations for this Canadian-built-and-designed marvel of cold ocean engineering. There was much to celebrate and, for many, to contemplate as this human sea surged above the blue waters of the Northumberland Strait. Until that

moment in history, that narrow arm of the Gulf of St. Lawrence had dominated and in many ways, defined life on the Island, Canada's smallest province.

The story of the bridge is a long journey from dream to reality. Under the Terms of Union when Prince Edward Island reluctantly joined Confederation on July 1, 1876, the federal government had vaguely promised "continuous means of communication between Prince Edward Island and the mainland would be maintained."

The only way to and from the mainland in those days was by open boat. In winter when the Northumberland Strait became choked with ice, this meant an arduous and sometimes perilous crossing. Passengers received a discount ($1.50 rather than $2 per round trip), if they

Facing page: Confederation Bridge crosses the Northumberland Strait at its narrowest point, between Borden, PEI (foreground), and Cape Jourimain, on the New Brunswick side, a distance of 12.9 kilometres.

The Mi'kmaq called Prince Edward Island, Abegweit, meaning "cradled on the waves." The namesake, CN ferry Abegweit crosses the Strait to the Island's red shores.

agreed to help the crew push and pull the small "ice boats" across the treacherous, shifting floes. It could be a ticket to disaster. In 1885, 15 passengers and 7 crew were caught in a blinding snowstorm and had to spend the night on the ice in 3 boats. Although there were no lives lost, one passenger became delirious and subsequently several lost limbs to frostbite. The incident renewed Islanders' urgent calls for a more reliable link to Canada.

One of the most outspoken supporters was Senator George Howlan. He urged the building of a rail tunnel under the seabed of the Strait. "We should never be imprisoned in the future as we have been in the past," he said. "Not only would the old industries be stimulated and put on a level with the other provinces, but quite a large number of new industries would be inaugurated." His arguments for a fixed

link were to be echoed many times in the century to follow.

Although Howlan's call for a rail tunnel went unheeded, car ferry service was inaugurated in 1917 by the coal-burning *S.S. Prince Edward Island*. Marine Atlantic ferries maintained the lifeline to the Island for 80 years, with occasional delays in winter due to wind and ice. Five generations of some families served this proud maritime tradition. In 1996, their

last full year of operations, the ferries carried more than two million passengers. But the desire for a permanent link to the mainland never went away.

The notion of a fixed link was revived in 1957 when it was proposed that a rock-fill causeway be built across the Strait, with a 300-metre bridge span to allow for the passage of ship traffic. Shipping interests opposed the plan as too danger-ous. The causeway concept was given

Ferry workers like Gerard Sexton, who worked on the vessels for 37 years, mourned the passing of a way of life when Marine Atlantic ended its eight decades of "faithful service." Six hundred and eighty full- and part-time workers lost their jobs.

second life in 1963, however, and work actually begun on approaches on both sides of the Strait. But, in 1969, the project was deemed too costly and abandoned.

Then, in 1985, the government received three unsolicited proposals for a fixed link from private companies. Feasibility studies were undertaken and public consultation initiated. In 1988, 60 per cent of Islanders approved further study of "a fixed link" in a plebiscite, though it was unclear whether such a link would take the form of a bridge, a tunnel, or a causeway. Friends of the Island—a group of fishers, farmers, ferry workers, and citizens who cherished their Island status —vigorously opposed a link of any kind, claiming it would threaten not only their livelihood but their Island "way of life."

Between September 1988, and May 1992, three proposals—all for bridges— were considered. As with any project of this scale, it was subject to a federal environmental review. The first report of the Federal Environmental Assessment Review Panel, issued in August 1990,

Construction of the bridge began in October, 1993. Because the Island consists mainly of red sandstone, everything needed for the project—stone, sand, and cement—was imported.

Facing page: The Buzzard, a jackup barge, was used for underwater (tremie) concreting of the pier bases to the bedrock.

actually recommended that the project not proceed, saying the risk of harmful effects was unacceptable. Damage to marine ecosystems and agricultural microclimates, due to delays in the movement of ice out of the Northumberland Strait in spring, were among the panel's primary concerns.

It seemed that the link would again be forestalled. In the end, however, the Minister of Public Works approved the bridge proposal of Strait Crossing Joint Venture (SCJV) as environmentally sound. The parties signed a public-private partnership agreement on October 7, 1993. Under terms of the agreement, SCJV would finance, build and operate the bridge, and the Government of Canada would make annual payments of $41.9 million to the builder for 35 years, after which the bridge would become the property of the federal government. A completion date of May 31, 1997 was set, even though detailed design work had yet to begin.

The casting yard at Borden, PEI, was an assembly line writ large, where most of the 183 bridge components were manufactured.

Facing page: Workers scale the rebar cages which formed the steel skeleton of the concrete bridge components.

Overleaf: The heavy lifting vessel Svanen *originally was built in 1990 for construction of the Store Baelt bridge in Denmark. It was made longer, higher and more buoyant before being towed across the Atlantic for work on Confederation Bridge.*

II

ICE, WIND, WAVES, AND TIDES
DESIGNING THE BRIDGE OF THE CENTURY

No bridge of this size and complexity had ever been built under conditions as harsh as those that prevail in the Northumberland Strait.

The builder Strait Crossing Joint Venture (SCJV), a consortium of Canadian, Dutch and French companies, had to design a bridge that had a probability of failure, due to any conditions, including the ice loads, which in any given year was one in ten million. Added to the overriding concern about ice were the other forces: wind, waves, tides, ship collisions, even earthquakes. Not only did the builder have to cope with these formidable forces of nature but, in keeping with federal government criteria, it had to design a bridge that would stand for 100 years, twice as long as the normal lifespan of a bridge, even in more equable climes. It was a daunting design challenge that, in the end, advanced the engineering of long-span bridges, and pushed Canadian technology to the forefront of cold ocean engineering.

International experts in industry, government, and academe were sought to help find a design that could address such environmental challenges. It was a monumental task. According to one ice expert, more effort was spent related to the ice engineering aspect of the bridge than has been spent on any other similar structure ever built.

When ice floes collide in the Strait, they tend to create large masses of compressed ice rubble. The largest of these ridges may

Facing page: Tidal currents push by the bridge piers in this narrow arm of the Gulf of St. Lawrence. Tides, ice, wind and waves were formidable environmental factors that the bridge designers had to take into account.

At the peak of production, the skyline of the casting yard at Borden bristled with silhouettes of cranes and finished concrete components.

have an underwater "keel," 20 metres deep, and a visible "sail," about the height of a two-storey house. The weight and momentum of such a formidable juggernaut tends to topple anything in its path.

A complex computer model simulated ice conditions the bridge might encounter. To acquire the real life data to feed into the computer, research teams helicoptered to the ice fields, extracted extensive ice cores from ridges and surveyed the sea floor itself for ice scours—trenches created where the ice keels gouge the bedrock.

To prevent a structural catastrophe due to "foundation failure," designers can either anchor a bridge by piles or rely on gravity, building the piers big enough to resist such forces by virtue of their own weight. Confederation Bridge combines these strategies. The shorter and less massive nearshore piers are anchored by piles sunk 6 to 11 metres into the underlying bedrock. The main bridge piers, however, are massive enough to be free-standing.

The combined weight of the pier-and-girder unit is well in excess of 10,000 tonnes (the equivalent of about 20,000

compact cars), more than enough to resist a maximum ice force of 3,000 tonnes, expected to occur only once in 10,000 years.

The original design called for cylindrical piers, which are the most economical to build. Ice, by nature, is strong in compression but weak in tension—it is harder to crush it than to bend it. An ice floe meeting a cylindrical pier straight on would go into compression, increasing resistance. The solution—install a cone-shaped ice shield at the bottom of each pier shaft. The partly submerged ice shield forces ice floes to ride up the side of

the pier, in effect bending them and causing them to crack. The ice shields have not only withstood the ice floes but cut them like a harrow, confirming predictions made with laboratory models.

With the ice migrating back and forth across the Strait it was important not only to determine what would happen when ice encountered the bridge, but how the bridge might affect the ice dynamics in the entire waterway. Every year, impressive rubble piles build up on both sides of the Strait, where they serve to anchor the ice floes to the shore. Whether or not the

Construction workers—90 per cent of whom were Atlantic Canadians— worked in highly efficient crews, each producing a specific bridge component.

Overleaf: The completed bridge consists of 22 individual box girder units, in effect, 22 little bridges of two main girders each, joined by 60-metre, drop-in spans.

bridge piers are going to increase the amount of rubble that piles up remains to be seen. In future years, ice piles will be monitored to determine whether they are bigger or smaller with the bridge in place.

The unanswered question from the beginning of the project has been whether the bridge will hold ice in the Strait longer in the spring and, if so, what effects that would have on fisheries and the local microclimate so critical to agriculture on PEI.

Studies carried out by the Ice Climatology Division of Environment Canada's Ice Centre in Ottawa indicated a worst case scenario of a two-week ice-out delay due to ice jamming. Normally, there is a great variability in the timing of ice leaving the Strait—it may occur as early as late March or as late as early May. However, late ice-out appears to have little effect on summer water temperatures, and late ice, such as occurred in 1984, did not seem to affect catch levels in the $100-million Northumberland Strait fishery for lobsters, scallops, mackerel, and herring.

Even so, to decrease probability of ice jamming, and therefore ice-out delays, SCJV decided to increase the distance between piers from 175 to 250 metres. This configuration, coupled with the pier design, is expected to delay ice-out in the Strait no more than two days, once in a hundred years.

Studies indicated that the bridge would cause a maximum of a two-week delay in the timing of ice leaving the Strait, with little or no effect on the $100-million Northumberland Strait fishery for lobster, scallops, mackerel, and herring.

Facing page: The high-strength concrete ice cone at the bottom of each bridge pier is designed to bend ice floes, causing them to crack and break up. To date, the piers have cut the ice floes as predicted.

SCJV's efforts to mitigate possible environmental impacts earned the 1994 Environmental Achievement Award from the Canadian Construction Association. With a project of this scale, however, environmental consequences cannot be entirely avoided.

Not only ice moves back and forth through the Strait, but large populations of migratory birds. A half million aquatic birds of 25 species, including eiders, gannets, mergansers, loons, and scoters, funnel through the Strait in spring and fall. All coastal structures, including lighthouses, are a hazard to migrating birds. Collisions with the bridge, especially during foul weather, are inevitable. To reduce bird mortality, SCJV opted for a lighting system least likely to attract birds. Rather than the continuous rail lighting often used in tunnels, regular light standards, spaced as far apart as possible, are shielded to direct light downward, thereby minimizing the likelihood of bird strikes.

The other challenge to designers in the Strait was wind, which itself drives the ice. The bridge sits astride one of the windiest spots in Canada. The University of Western Ontario's Boundary Layer Wind Tunnel Lab was called upon to provide answers on how to manage the

A launching truss was used to place smaller pre-cast elements for the approaches to the bridge on the PEI side.

Facing page: Bridge components cure in the casting yard. All elements of the bridge are made of high performance concrete that is resistant to ice abrasion and the corrosive action of salt water.

The heavy lifting vessel Svanen *lowers a 192-metre-long main girder, weighing 7,500 tonnes, into position. All bridge components had to be of a size and weight that could be handled by the* Svanen.

troubling winds that blow through nature's own wind tunnel—the unobstructed Strait.

Testing involved collecting comprehensive meteorological data from Maritime wind stations and the ferry terminuses, building a sophisticated 1:250 scale model that responded in the same way as the real bridge, and subjecting it to appropriate wind forces. It was the first time that scale models had been used not merely as a check on the safety of an

existing design of a long-span bridge, but to determine what that design should be to ensure a safe, durable structure.

The wind studies also contributed to considerations of driver safety. While the incorporation of a 1.1-metre high, solid barrier will partly obscure the view of the Strait for most car drivers, it will protect against gusty winds that swirl 40-60 metres above sea level. For trucks, exposed to the Strait's winds, speed limits will protect against overturning. The maximum limit will be 80 kilometres an

hour and be incrementally reduced by 20 kilometres an hour as the wind speeds reach 20, 40 and 60 kilometres an hour.

The roadbed was also designed to curve in the form of a driver-friendly, flattened-S. Experts believe that a straight road can have a hypnotic effect and consequently cause more accidents.

Another critical design question was what the bridge should be made of—steel or concrete? Steel is susceptible to rust (especially in a saltwater environment)

and using it would make it difficult to meet the 100-year-design-life requirement. However, concrete of sufficient strength to withstand ice and other forces in the Strait had never been manufactured outside the laboratory, let alone on such a grand scale.

It became necessary to push the realm of concrete technology a whole dimension ahead of where it had been at the outset of the project. The key was to create a high performance concrete that would be resistant to ice abrasion and the corrosive

Each girder was eased on to the top of the pier shaft within millimetres of a set point with the aid of a specially modified global positioning system (GPS) aided by eight to ten satellites orbiting 20,000 kilometres above the earth.

action of salt water and other elements but that could still be easily shaped and handled.

With only red sandstone available from the Island, all materials for the concrete—stone, sand and cement—were ferried across the Strait to the pre-cast facility at Borden. The concrete contains cubical-shaped stone, with a rough irregular surface specially manufactured at a plant in Nova Scotia, rather than conventional gravel with its sharp, flat edges. The irregular stone surface provides maximum strength while an unusual mixture of additives, including fly ash, silica fume, and a plasticizing agent, created a mixture that was easy to work with and capable of withstanding the Northumberland Strait environment.

Tests showed that the main structural elements have twice the strength of those in a conventional bridge; the ice shields are tougher yet, being five to six times as strong as the concrete in a house basement, for example. Before beginning construction, however, a full-size mockup of a bridge unit was built and stressed until it failed, confirming that the numbers not only worked on paper but in the real world.

Except in winter, when ice clogged the Strait, work on the bridge proceeded around the clock, with one component being placed every day.

Facing page: The three steps necessary for the erection of each box girder are shown here. The Betty L, crane barge (foreground), excavates the bedrock prior to pier placement; the Buzzard, a jackup barge (middle), concretes a base to the bedrock, the Svanen (background) lowers a main girder on to a pier base.

III

STRETCHING THE IMAGINATION
HOW THE BRIDGE WAS BUILT

The scale of the Confederation Bridge stretches the imagination. More than three times the volume of concrete went into the bridge than was used in construction of Toronto's SkyDome. At 12.9 km it is nearly twice as long as the San Francisco-Oakland Bay Bridge (6.8 km) and one-quarter longer than the 9.9 km Seto Ohashi Bridge in Japan, the largest bridge built in the 1980s. Each main girder weighs 7,500 tonnes—equivalent to 1,500 elephants—and is 192 metres in length, longer than two football fields.

In total, there were 183 massive components—girders, drop-in girders, pier bases, and pier shaft/iceshields—to move from the casting facility in Borden-Carleton to the installation site on the water.

For all of the complexities and ingenuities of the design, building the bridge was constrained, first and foremost, by the equipment available. All of the components had to be of a size and weight that could be handled by the heavy-lifting vessel *Svanen*.

The *Svanen* is a unique vessel, designed for just such Herculean tasks. In profile its towering gantry makes the vessel look like a giant, mechanical swan—thus its Danish name. A 103-metre-long, C-shaped catamaran, it was built in 1990 to construct the Store Baelt bridge, connecting mainland Denmark with some of its islands, and was made longer, higher, and more buoyant for the heavier work on this side of the Atlantic. Without it, Confederation Bridge simply could not have been built.

Facing page: The bridge soars 40 metres—11 storeys—above the Northumberland Strait and 60 metres at the central navigation span. A helicopter (right) carries supplies to workers on the bridge deck.

Overleaf: The completed Confederation Bridge curves in a driver-friendly, S-shape across the 12.9 kilometre-wide Northumberland Strait. The bridge is curved in order to eliminate the hypnotic effect of a straight roadbed, and thus reduces the potential for accidents.

Placement of each element demanded not only brute force but hair-breadth, military precision. With the aid of a specially modified global positioning system (GPS), each girder was eased into place onto the top of the pier shaft within millimetres of a set point. GPS receivers at either end of the girder and at the top of the 100-metre-high gantry collected data from 8 to 10 satellites (orbiting 20,000 kilometres above the earth), pinpointing the exact location. Each placement was akin to "a lunar landing," according to one of the 23-person *Svanen* crew.

First, the mammoth components had to be moved from the casting facility, where they were poured, to the jetty where they were picked up by the *Svanen*. This task was managed by the "Lobster" and the "Turtle"—special transport sleds that look like tanks on rails.

The 60-hectare casting yard in Borden-Carleton was an assembly line writ large. At peak production, 15 cranes figured the skyline; the yard was stacked with the colossal components, some clad in wooden forms, others bristling with steel

Pier bases, in various stages of completion, (left), wait their trip on special transport sleds to the jetty, on stainless steel, Teflon-coated rails (right).

rebar, others complete waiting their ride on Teflon-coated, stainless steel tracks to the jetty.

A main girder went through a dozen separate stages, with each production cycle taking eight days and the complete manufacture of a girder taking three months. By the second year of the project, one bridge component per day was rolling off the line.

The completed bridge consists of 22 individual box girder units, in effect, 22 little bridges of two main girders each, joined by 60-metre, drop-in spans. Every other span is hinged, so that in the event of a destructive impact, it drops out, thus preventing a domino-effect—called "progressive collapse." The hinges also allow for expansion and contraction under normal temperature changes. All

Each main girder went through a dozen separate stages, with each production cycle taking 8 days and the complete manufacture of a girder taking 3 months. "Now you know how the pyramids were built," joked Kevin Pytyck, manager of contract requirements.

Facing page: The Svanen's 100-metre-high gantry makes the vessel look like a giant mechanical swan—thus its Danish name.

bridge components, except for the hinged drop-ins, are tied together by cables running through the concrete that function as an internal skeleton. When stretched taught like piano wire—a technique called post-tensioning—the cables increase the strength and durability of the concrete.

The last of the monumental main girders was set in place on November 19, 1996, at 11:30 P.M., completing one of the longest continuous span bridges in the world, on time, and the final cost was $1 billion.

Despite its imposing size, the finished bridge has an almost delicate appearance. Cantilevered 40 metres—11 storeys—above the Northumberland Strait (60 metres at the central navigation span), it curves in an aesthetically pleasing shape, shore to shore. Drivers will now make the trip in 12 minutes, compared to the 45-minute to hour-long crossing by ferry.

The last main girder was set in place on November 19, 1996, at 11:30 P.M., completing one of the longest continuous multi-span bridges in the world.

Facing page: Main girders are connected to each other by smaller drop-in spans. Every other span is hinged, so that in the event of a destructive impact, it drops out, thus preventing a domino-effect called progressive collapse.

IV

EPILOGUE

BRIDGE TO THE FUTURE

Some will miss the ferry connection to the Island. Nearly three-quarters of visitors to the Island considered the ferry ride a prime tourist attraction in itself. For those who choose to, they can still make the passage to the Island by water aboard the ferry that plies between Caribou, Nova Scotia, and Wood Islands, PEI. But for most, crossing Confederation Bridge will become the preferred way to reach the Island's red sandstone shores. More than a million visitors are expected to cross Confederation Bridge every year.

Among truckers, who daily carry goods to and from the Island, there has been very little doubt whether Confederation Bridge is a good thing. There will be no lineups, and no limitations on the capacity of the Bridge to accommodate them, as there were with the ferries—though there will be times when high winds will delay their travel.

For Islanders who opposed any permanent link to their Island home, there is lingering concern that the Bridge will rob the Island of its identity which, in the words of Island historian David Weale, is "profoundly tied up with its insularity."

The question is, when is an island no longer a real island, but one in name only? Only time will tell how Confederation Bridge will change Island life—but it surely will.

The Mi'kmaq first crossed the Northumberland Strait to make their home, 8,500 to 9,500 years ago. They called the red, crescent-shaped island, *Abegweit*,

Facing page: The completion of Confederation Bridge signals the dawn of a new era on Prince Edward Island.

Overleaf: Confederation Bridge soars above the pastoral landscape of Prince Edward Island. While the fixed link promises increased trade and tourism, it will also bring changes to the Island's rural lifestyle.

meaning "cradled on the waves." When the first European of record, Jacques Cartier, cruised its shores in 1534 he described it as "the fairest land that may possibly be seen." He would have looked upon its famous north shore beaches, barrier islands, dunes, and marsh-jewelled estuaries—which still elicit the praise of first-time, and long-time, visitors.

To many Canadians, Prince Edward Island has its unique place in history as the Cradle of Confederation. It was at The Charlottetown Conference of 1864 that the notion of Canada was first discussed.

While Canada's seventh province is the smallest, with its population constituting less than one per cent of the national total,

it is also the most densely populated. The landscape is a neighbourly collection of family farms, separated by fertile fields. The Island's pastoral nature has given rise to yet another descriptive name, Garden of the Gulf. Much of the original Acadian forest has been cleared and replaced by a beguiling and productive patchwork of fields—many seeded to potatoes. The pattern of the land, with its red soils always at the centre, reminds one of the traditional Log Cabin quilt. It is a place equally shaped by nature, on its seaward verges, as by human toil in the interior. The late Island poet Milton Acorn said it best, when he wrote: "Nowhere that plowcut worms heal themselves in red

A monument at Gateway Village in Borden commemorates the contribution of some 2,500 construction workers who built the Confederation Bridge.

Facing page: More than 20,000 walked and ran across the bridge to celebrate its opening on May 31, 1997. It is hoped that the bridge will boost out-of-province visitors from 740,000 to more than a million per year.

loam; spruces squat in sand or the stones of a river rattle its dark tunnel under elms is a spot not measured by hands."

For many people worldwide, the island is Anne's Island, a place forever associated with the orphan heroine of Lucy Maud Montgomery's novels. Montgomery built a lasting link to readers around the world, based on love of her native Island. Her words will stand as reminders of the values and virtues of Island life.

Whatever changes it may bring, Confederation Bridge is an accomplishment in its own right, one that has provided a tangible link for the Island to the continent, and vice versa. This wonder of modern engineering will likely stand for more than a century, as a monument to the labours and ingenuity of the 6,000 men and women—engineers, construction workers, mariners, and scientists— who designed, tested and built it.

The fine photos collected here by Islanders Wayne Barrett and Anne MacKay count as a considerable achievement in themselves and provide a valuable record of that remarkable undertaking for future generations.

Framed by a bridge component, Gateway Village in Borden welcomes bridge travellers to the Island.

Facing page: Confederation Bridge is designed to last 100 years but will likely endure much longer. The builder will operate the Bridge for 35 years after which ownership of the bridge will be transferred to the federal government.

Overleaf: The Bridge will now carry most visitors to the famous beaches of PEI.